26x 11/15 2

THE
PUEBLO INDIANS

The
PUEBLO INDIANS
Farmers of the Rio Grande

By SONIA BLEEKER

Illustrated by Patricia Boodell

WILLIAM MORROW & COMPANY

New York · 1955

Grateful recognition is given to
Mr. Stanley A. Stubbs,
Museum of New Mexico, Santa Fe, New Mexico,
for reading and criticizing the manuscript.

14   15

For
Elisabeth Bevier Hamilton

CONTENTS

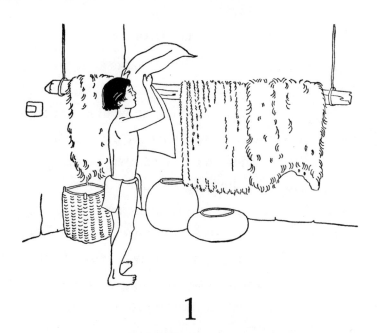

1

HOME

I<small>T</small> <small>IS</small> good to be home, Young Hawk thought, throwing off the soft rabbitskin blanket that covered him, yawning and stretching on the heavy buffalo robe under him. He sat up and rubbed his naked thighs, tucked in and tied his breechcloth, and stood up. He was an Indian boy of one of the Rio Grande pueblos, about twelve winters old, lean and round-faced with thick black hair.

Young Hawk folded the blankets and, holding them in his arms, looked up at the familiar low ceiling and the three heavy pine beams that supported it. Mother must have whitewashed the walls while Father and I were away trading, he thought, noticing how smooth and clean the walls were—free of cracks and flyspecks.

Young Hawk walked over to the pine pole that was suspended by two heavy, twisted yucca cords from a beam in the ceiling, forming a rug hanger along the entire length of wall. The hanger was filled with blankets, since everyone in the household except himself was already up. The boy swung the folded length of the buffalo robe over his head and tossed it over the pole. He threw the narrow rabbitskin blanket on top of it and straightened the ends of the two blankets so they were even. Mother liked to see the blankets hung neatly and evenly on the hanger, and Young Hawk wanted to please her today, since he had been away from home for over two moons.

Young Hawk's home was simply furnished. Tables and chairs were unknown to the Indians three to four hundred years ago. A family sat on the earth floor or on mats made of yucca leaves. They slept on buffalo robes and rabbitskin blankets. These Indians of the Rio Grande got the buffalo robes by trading for them with the Indians of the plains, who hunted buffalo. The rabbitskin blankets were made by the pueblo men. The skins were cut into long, narrow strips; then the strips were tied together and stretched between two poles, squared to the right width and length of the finished blanket. The men pulled thread spun of yucca fiber or cedar bark between the strips of fur. This made a warm, light blanket.

Now Young Hawk could hear the muffled sound of corn being ground in the small room next door. Mother and Grandmother must be hard at work. Very important in each household were the grinding stones, or *metates* (meh-ta-

tays). Each family usually had two or three of these large, flat stones. Daily the women of the household knelt over them to grind corn into meal. At one side of the living room or in a small dark room next to it, the family stored some of its corn after it had been harvested and dried.

On getting up each morning, a woman shelled a few ears of corn into a basket. She then knelt in front of her *metate*, threw a handful of kernels

on it and, holding a smaller stone in both her hands, passed it up and down, crushing the corn kernels. If she wanted finer corn meal, she ground the meal a second time. She sifted the fine meal through a basket sieve till she had produced evenly ground corn meal to her liking.

Young Hawk had spoken only a few words to his mother when he and Father had returned home the night before from two months' visiting and trading among the neighboring villages, or pueblos, on the Rio Grande and westward into Navaho country. On their return, Mother had immediately busied herself making a fire in the small firepit in the center of the room. Crouching low, she had fanned the flame with a plaited cornhusk fan till the dry juniper twigs caught fire from the hot ashes in the fireplace. Next she put a large clay pot full of corn-meal mush close to the fire to warm for the travelers' evening meal.

That had been last night. Now Young Hawk looked outdoors. The sun was just a quarter up

the sky and the open square of Kishtaya, Young
Hawk's pueblo, was flooded with sunshine. The
day would be hot and people were already seeking
the shade—what there was of it. The houses,
built on the four sides of the square, or plaza,
stood close together. They were two stories high,
made of sun-dried clay, or adobe. A thick, smooth
coat of clay covered them on the outside. The
second story of each house was built a few feet
narrower than the first, leaving a narrow space in
front. Ladders led up to the second stories. Pairs

of tall ladder poles pointing at the blue sky
studded the flat roofs of the houses.

Kishtaya was built on a high flat-topped rock,
or mesa, not far from the river—the Rio Grande
del Norte in what is now New Mexico. There
was little soil on this mesa for trees to grow in.
In hot weather the only shade in the morning and
afternoon came from the houses themselves, and
at noon, when the sun shone directly overhead,
there was no shade at all. Everyone then went inside the cool homes to escape the heat. The thick-

walled adobe houses were cool even on a hot summer day. They were also warm in winter, when the cold winds blew freely across the mesa.

Along the banks of the Rio Grande were the cornfields of these River Indians. There were more than twenty of their pueblos, and they all looked very much like Kishtaya. The houses were made of adobe, with two or more stories, flat roofs, and ladder poles pointing up at the sky. The homes crowded around an open plaza, where the people of the pueblo met for ceremonials and dances. In each pueblo were several ceremonial houses, some of which were built underground, like cellars. These cellarlike buildings were called kivas.

The Indians of the many River pueblos lived peacefully together, visiting one another and trading. Each respected the others' farming lands. In times of drought or when a village needed more food in winter, it was usual for another pueblo to give food to tide the people over to the next harvest.

Many of these River pueblos still stand today. Some of the best known are Taos, Picuris, San Juan, Santa Clara, San Ildefonso, Cochiti, Santo Domingo, San Felipe, Sandia and Jemez, Zia, and Santa Ana. The Spaniards conquered all these villages in 1598 and they are still called by the names the Spaniards gave them. Some Spanish words introduced with the conquest have become part of our language—*pueblo*, for example, and *plaza*.

Looking out of the narrow doorway, Young Hawk could see women and girls coming out of their houses and going down the ladders on their morning errands. Those who were going for water to the river below carried large pots. As each woman came out of her doorway, she placed the pot on top of her head. Walking very straight, she climbed down the mesa toward the Rio Grande. The people used the river water for drinking, washing, and bathing, as well as for irrigating their cornfields and gardens.

In the clear air, Young Hawk could even see

women way down the valley, entering the narrow path in the dense growth of cottonwoods and bushes that bordered the bank of the river. Others were emerging, steadying the heavy pots on their heads, to begin their stately route back up the mesa. Some women carried large woven cotton bags. They were going down to their gardens in the valley below to get a squash or some beans for the evening meal, or some fresh green corn.

Young Hawk went inside the house and pushed aside the cotton curtain that separated the little room where Mother and Grandmother were working. Both women were kneeling in front of two large, sloping blocks of stone. Mother threw a handful of corn kernels upon her *metate*. Grasping another long, flat stone in both hands, she pushed it up and down over the corn, pressing down hard and crushing the kernels to a pulp. Then Grandmother took the meal Mother had ground, and ground it even finer on her stone.

The women's long bangs covered their faces as they bent over their *metates*. They shook their

heads and blew at the loose hair to keep it out
of their eyes as they worked. Mother was graceful and small—not much taller than Young
Hawk. Her long black hair was done up in a
heavy knot at the nape of her neck. Mother and
Grandmother were dressed alike in skirts woven
of yucca fiber. Both wore necklaces and earrings.
Mother's feet were so small that the moccasins
she wore were no bigger than a little girl's.

A neighbor sat on the floor near Grandmother
with four baskets of corn in front of her. Young
Hawk saw that she was shelling a different kind
of corn into each basket—yellow, blue, red, and
white. They are going to bake wafer bread for a
feast, he thought.

Mother got up from her grinding stone when
she saw Young Hawk. "It is good to have you
home, son," she said, moving toward the door.
"I'll get something for you to eat. Wait here."

Outside, protected by the low adobe wall, the
women did most of their cooking during the hot
summer months. Pieces of rabbit meat hung on

a beam, drying. Close to the wall stood cooking pots, bowls, and large storage pots, all of which Mother had made.

In the corner stood the familiar water jar. It was not watertight. Moisture seeped through its walls and this helped to keep the water fresh and cool. Young Hawk dipped the gourd that lay on the mouth of the pot into the water. He began to sip the cool water as he waited for Mother to call him.

Water was boiling in a pot and Mother poured in a few handfuls of parched corn meal, which she took from a covered jar. She stirred it for a few minutes and then told Young Hawk to come and eat. Before he tasted the hot nourishing liquid, Young Hawk was careful to do as Father had taught him. Taking a pinch of corn meal from a bowl near the wall, he sprinkled it into the fire as an offering to the spirits. Then he dipped a large clay spoon into the pot and sipped his breakfast.

Corn had been the mainstay of these Indian

farmers ever since they could remember. It must have been grown by the Indians of the Southwest for thousands of years. Although they did not know as much as our farmers today about how plants grow and reproduce, the Indians had made big strides in domesticating plants. Through the many centuries, with the sons doing as they had seen their fathers do, they had grown corn of different colors—yellow, blue, red, white, black, and streaked varieties.

Once long ago, a legend says, meat was the people's main food. But then came a drought, because the rain gods would not let the rain come. All the forests burned and the game died. The people were left starving. Men and women went out daily into the meadows and picked up any wild plants they could find, but that was not enough to keep them from starving. The medicine men danced and prayed for rain. At last Mother Earth told them what to do. The medicine men put six pebbles of different colors into a hole and covered up the hole with a large stone.

Again they danced and prayed, for four weeks. And one day when the chief of the pueblo removed the large stone and looked into the hole, he found six corn plants in it. These they set out in six widely separated fields and from them developed six kinds of corn, each one a different color from all the others. To this day the people plant the different kinds of corn in separate parts of their fields, to keep the color strains from mixing.

2

THE CORNFIELDS

DAWN was just beginning to tint the sky as Young
Hawk, following closely behind his father, the
War Chief, walked down the narrow, winding
path that led from Kishtaya to the fields by the

river. Behind them came other men and boys, walking softly on their moccasined feet. Each one carried his gardening tool, a hoe made of bone or a flat stone tied to a thin pole; his gourd full of water; and a small bag containing parched corn or a roll of wafer bread. Some of the men and most of the boys also carried their bows and arrows. They did not plan to go hunting, but a deer might wander across the field toward the river for a drink, or a rabbit might leap out of the brush. Meat was always welcome at home, and so was a good buckskin or the skin of a rabbit.

The spring rains had swelled the Rio Grande till it overflowed its banks. It had washed some of the top soil from the Kishtaya fields and in the low places it had deposited sand. This the men must scrape away. It took a great deal of time.

The men also had to rebuild the narrow irrigation ditches so the water would flow evenly in between the rows of corn. They knew that this work would have to be repeated many, many times during the spring and summer months, from one end of each field to the other, after every downpour. A man had to watch constantly to be sure that each corn plant had a firm base of hoed soil.

Growing corn was one of the main tasks of these pueblo farmers. The time for planting the corn was determined each year by the Pueblo Chief. On that day all the men went to the fields together, and the women came to help them. The men dug the holes with digging sticks and the women dropped in the seed. The men believed that if their wives helped in the corn planting they would get a better crop, since women bear children and so must have the power that makes things grow.

After the young cornstalks leafed and thickened, the fields were weeded and irrigated carefully, and then beans and squash were sowed between the rows of corn. When the time arrived for husking the ears of corn, everyone helped with the task. It was a happy holiday time. The husked corn was hung on poles or spread on logs to dry. When the corn was dry, each family piled some of it, as we pile wood, in a small storage room in their house. The remainder they put in storage pits on the outskirts of the pueblo.

Particularly good ears of corn of one variety were often traded for ears of another variety that a man wanted to grow the following year. Ears of corn to be used for seed received special care. The men were responsible for them, and the rest of the family never touched these ears. Seed corn was usually a pure variety, but although the men were careful, white kernels always crept in with the colored kernels. Not only did the men of Kishtaya exchange ears of corn among themselves; quite often they traded their seed corn for varieties they liked in neighboring pueblos.

All the corn except the seed corn belonged to the women. A man could trade the seed corn as he wished, but he had to ask his wife's permission if he wanted any of the stored corn. Young Hawk and the other boys who grew corn in their fields gave their harvest to their mothers.

The women watched over the stored corn. They constantly turned the ears to expose every side to the air and they took advantage of sunny days to dry them. Each woman knew just about how much corn her family would need before the next harvest. If she had more than enough, she ground more corn for daily use and her family enjoyed bigger meals. If she feared she would not have enough to last till the fall, she economized. She ground less corn for each day's meals, tried to serve more meat, and used more berries and wild plants to keep her family fed.

No part of the corn was ever thrown away. The men and women dried and saved the cornhusks, for they made excellent wrappings for different kinds of corn bread and were used in rolling cigarettes and making mats. Corncobs made excellent kindling, as well as firewood for firing pottery. Men and boys carved corncobs for pipes, for toys, and for games.

The bean and squash harvests were important too. The beans were shelled, spread out on yucca mats to dry in the sun, and then put into large storage baskets. Beans were boiled with stews or ground and mixed with parched corn and corn meal, forming an important part of the Indians' diet.

Much of the squash was eaten fresh. When drying squash, a woman scraped and peeled off the skin, cut an opening at one end, and took out the seeds. Then she cut the squash into several strips and hung it to dry. When it was thoroughly dried, she tied the strips of squash into bundles and put them away in the storage room. Sometimes she dried the squash whole.

The dried squash had to be watched constantly to make sure it did not get moldy. At the first sign of mold, a woman removed the squash from the storage basket so it would not spoil the others. She then scraped off the forming mold and boiled the squash for a meal. Fresh squash was often baked, but the dried squash tasted best when boiled.

The River Indians kept improving their ways

of farming, enlarging their irrigation ditches so they could plant more and more corn, beans, and squash. Relatives often stored their corn, dried beans, and squash in large communal storage pits. In case of drought, the people usually managed to stretch their stored food for an extra year.

Because of their ample food supply, the pueblo farmers were the envy of wandering tribes to the east and west, north and south. They called these raiders Apache, which means strangers or enemies. Bands of these nomads formerly had raided the pueblos continuously, running off with baskets of stored food and capturing women and children, whom they used as slaves. To escape the Apache raiders, the River Indians had long ago moved their homes away from their cornfields and some had built their pueblos high on the flat-topped mesas.

To anyone looking up from below at the high mesa on which the village was built, the walls of the houses seemed to merge with the walls of the cliffs. It was hard to tell that there was a pueblo on top. The ladders were always pulled up at night. They were also hastily pulled up when strangers were sighted below. No one could get near the mesa without being seen from the top. Lookouts—boys or men—kept watch when the War Chief heard rumors of raiders. Unwelcome strangers were greeted with speeding arrows or with heavy boulders thrown with practiced and perfect aim. Raiders were usually put to flight.

It always seemed to Young Hawk, hoeing alongside his father, that no sooner did a man finish hoeing his cornfield than it was time to start again at the beginning. This year, Young Hawk had been given a small piece of land of his own, so he had to cultivate it in addition to helping Father.

The hot sun beat down mercilessly on the backs of the hoeing men as they moved down the field side by side, working rhythmically. Sometimes Young Hawk thought he could not stand another moment of the heat. His thick headband was soaked through with sweat. His arms ached. He had long ago drunk all the cool water he had brought along with him and he was still thirsty.

Yet, like the others, Young Hawk did not dare to complain about the sun's heat, even in the

silence of his own thoughts. The sun was an important god and very powerful. In spring the sun brought warmth and life to the soil after its cold winter rest. It might anger the god to know that a farmer complained about the heat, and then the sun might withhold his warm rays, or perhaps never return again.

As the sun rose high in the sky, the men put down their hoes one by one and went over to the cottonwood trees that lined the banks of the Rio Grande. There they lay down in the shade to cool off, rest a little, and eat their simple lunches. Most of them went down to the river, refilled their gourds, and poured their parched corn meal into them. In the cool shade they slowly drank the mixture, then lay down for a rest and talk.

This was a good time for the men to discuss their farming and ask one another about village affairs. They were tired after a day's work in the fields, so few festivals or dances were held in the pueblos during the busy spring and summer months. Most of the men stayed home after dark, since they had to get up again at dawn each day to return to the fields.

As the War Chief and Young Hawk stopped to rest, the boy looked at his father. The War Chief knew the boy's thoughts. "Go ahead, son," he said. "I see your friends by the river. Come back to the field when you are ready."

With a leap Young Hawk raced off. He quickly pulled off his moccasins and breechcloth and jumped into the cool water. Several boys were already splashing about. One of them picked up a piece of driftwood and threw it as far as he could. All the boys raced upstream to recover it. An older boy was the first to reach it. He held it up for everyone to see and then threw it as far as he could downstream. Again the boys lined up and raced after it. Tired as they were, the men resting under the cottonwoods sat up as they heard the boys shout. Fathers and uncles became so interested in the race that they left the cool shade and went down to the riverbank to watch and shout encouragement.

Having cooled off, the boys came out of the water and started a game of *tawaka* to dry off. It was a favorite summertime game, since the Indians believed that playing *tawaka* helped to bring on rain. They played the game barefooted, using two sticks of different colors, which one of the boys had brought along. Each stick was the

size of a man's finger. The boys divided into two
opposing teams and each team took turns kicking
its stick in a wide circle. Whichever team finished
the circle first won that round of the game. One
of them kept score by tying knots in two pieces
of yucca rope.

"Come, it is time to return to the field," the
War Chief said to the men. The boys stopped
playing, but their elders nodded to them to continue the game. Rain was needed and this game
would help. Young Hawk played on with the

other boys for a short time, then went back to work and worked till sunset.

Already it felt cooler and Young Hawk was thinking of food. Wafer bread was his favorite, especially when it was fresh. His mother had told him she would bake it that day, and it made him hungry to think about it.

Most women made this wafer bread once a week. Wafer bread was yellow, blue, red, or white, depending on the color of the corn that was used. Sometimes the women added vegetable dyes to the batter to make a deeper color.

Young Hawk's mother had ground blue corn flour the day before. Early in the morning after the men left for the field, she had mixed the finely ground blue corn meal with water and some ashes. Then she built a fire under the large flat baking stone. When the slab of stone became hot, Mother greased it with bear fat and poured some batter on it, spreading it very thin with her hand. In a few moments the batter was baked sufficiently and Mother peeled it off and put it on a flat basket tray. She then poured another layer of batter on the stone slab. Soon the second layer was done, and Mother put the first layer on top of the second and let it bake for another minute or two. Then she removed both layers and poured a third layer on the hot stone slab.

As the third layer baked, Mother put the first two layers on top of it and after a few moments removed the three layers together. She did the same with a fourth layer. Then she put the four layers aside and started all over again till the bowl of batter was empty. Finally she folded the baked layers into squares and rolled them into tight cylinders. The wafer bread was ready to eat. It was crisp, crunchy, and sweet. In a few days this wafer bread would be stale and would lose its taste, but it would not be wasted. Mother would crumble it into boiling water and make corn-meal mush from it.

As Young Hawk had expected, the smell of the fresh wafer bread filled the house when he and Father returned home that evening. Young

Hawk could hardly wait to sit down to the evening meal. Father seemed just as anxious, because he smelled his favorite dish too—corn cakes with meat and onions. The women had gathered the wild onions that grew by the river. Mother mixed white corn meal and water and dropped balls of the batter into boiling water. She took the balls out when they were ready and let them cool. Then she wrapped each ball in cornhusks, together with a piece of meat and some onion, and placed it on a hot stone to bake. She covered each cake with a hot stone to flatten it and cook it evenly on both sides.

The family ate in silence. Mother wiped and cleared away the bowls and spoons. Young Hawk could not keep his eyes open. He got up and looked outside. The stars were twinkling in the cloudless sky. All was quiet.

Inside, Mother set to work making mats of yucca leaves, pounding them rhythmically with small stones. Father picked up his spindle and some yucca fiber which he had prepared by soak-

ing and then pounding yucca leaves until they shredded. Rolling the spindle against his thigh, he twisted the moistened fibers into thread. But before long his eyes were closing too.

Mother spread a buffalo robe on the floor for
Father and helped Young Hawk with his robe.
The boy stretched out and fell asleep almost at
once.

3

THE RABBIT HUNT

Ever since the River Indians could remember, they had hunted rabbits. Deer, antelope, and bear were hunted too, on both sides of the Rio Grande, but rabbits were very abundant and were therefore the chief game. Men and boys went out daily throughout the year with clubs and rabbit sticks to hunt rabbits.

The men made the curved rabbit sticks. Each stick was a thin, flat piece of wood, hacked off a curved branch. A man rubbed the stick smooth with sandstone. Then he added notches at one

end for a good grip, and carved a design so he would recognize his stick when he went hunting with other people. A favorite design copied the beak and claws of a hawk, since, according to legend, the hawk had first taught people to use the rabbit stick.

Whenever meat was needed for a festival, the people of Kishtaya held a communal rabbit hunt in which everyone, young and old, took part. These hunts were usually held in the fall after the crops were in. Then the rabbits were fat after a summer of good feeding.

Before dawn on the day set for a rabbit hunt at Kishtaya, several scouts, led by Young Hawk's father, set out to find good hunting grounds for jack rabbits. They climbed down the mesa and then turned away from the river and toward the mountains. The sky was paling with the dawn and the grays, purples, and reds of the cliffs began to show.

The air was still cold and the scouts trotted fast to keep warm. They were naked except for breechcloths and buckskin moccasins. Most of them had bands of woven fiber on their heads to keep their shoulder-length hair out of their eyes. All had tucked rabbit sticks into their belts. The medicine men had prayed over these sticks the night before and had sprinkled corn meal on them. This was to bring good luck to the hunters. Each scout also carried a long pole.

The scouts trotted over rolling country filled with the smell of the pale-green sagebrush that grew in bunches over the plain. They skirted the rabbit brush and the evergreen dwarfed junipers, heavy with blue berries. At last they reached a wide level field with cliffs rising to the west of it. This was the place they had in mind for the hunt.

The scouts stuck the tall poles into the ground to serve as markers. While waiting for the crowd, they lay down in the grass to rest and eat a few mouthfuls of the parched corn they had brought along.

Soon after sunrise messengers went to every house in Kishtaya and told the people to come to the rabbit hunt. The villagers always waited for these messengers before leaving their homes. Every event in a pueblo was always announced by a messenger, who went to each house and notified the people.

They looked forward to hunting rabbits as great fun, even though it was strenuous. The rabbit hunt appealed particularly to the boys and girls of the pueblos because it gave them a chance to go on a real hunt with the grownups. Many of the boys and girls were excellent runners, almost as good as the experienced hunters. Although boys often left the pueblo on hunting or exploring trips, the girls were usually homebound. Except for short trips to the river for water or to gather dry wood for their cooking fires and wild plants and berries to flavor their corn mush, they seldom left the pueblo. Now they enjoyed getting far away from home.

A gay crowd soon formed on its way to the field. The men and boys were dressed like the scouts. Each carried a rabbit stick which had been blessed by the medicine men the night before. Some of the younger men and boys had clubs newly carved with rounded heads and tapering ends so they would fit comfortably into a man's hand.

The women and girls wore their best skirts and necklaces and earrings made of bone or stone. The women's hair was done up in a knot at the nape of the neck. The girls wore their hair in two round flattened knots, one on either side of the face. Younger girls were dressed like their mothers, but wore their hair in braids. They all carried bags and baskets full of food. None of the women carried clubs or sticks, for their job was to recover the rabbits after they were hit.

The crowd spread over the plain. Men and women took their places in twos and threes near a bush or a dwarfed juniper. They stood still, ears and eyes alert for the movement of a rabbit in the grass.

Young Hawk and his friends also took their positions in the field. Each took a rabbit stick from his belt and held it ready to throw. Suddenly a horned lizard on a boulder attracted their attention. Its coloring merged so well with the sandstone boulder that it had almost escaped their notice. The odd, flattened, spiny-armored creature was sunning itself.

"He, too, is a hunter," Young Hawk said, watching the lizard's round, beadlike eyes.

The lizard seemed asleep, yet it was alert and watchful. In a flash, as an unsuspecting ant came near it on its busy way up the boulder, the lizard's quick tongue shot out. With a snap, the ant disappeared inside the wide mouth.

"Let's take him home." One of the boys reached for his buckskin bag, opened it, and looked inside, hesitating. He had two corncakes in it for his midday meal. He and another boy put their corncakes into one bag, and the lizard was safely tied into the second bag to become their common property and pet.

The people formed an immense circle. Soon the crouching figures merged with the landscape. A newcomer on the scene would not have suspected that there were almost a hundred people in the field. Yet each man, crouching down, holding a club or stick in his hands, was alert and ready to strike at the first sign of any movement in the grass. Every woman and girl was equally alert, ready to jump up after a rabbit stick had hit its mark.

The long-eared jack rabbits are good runners and can leap great distances on their long hind legs. An Indian could not outrun a jack rabbit, so he had to outwit it. When alarmed, the jack rabbit, turning its ears to catch the danger sounds, leaps off through the grass. The hunter waited for this movement and then hurled his rabbit stick as the rabbit leaped.

Young Hawk saw a man hurl his stick at a jack rabbit as it bounded up out of the brush. The stick missed the first rabbit, but on the rebound hit another that had jumped up in alarm after the first. The rabbit went down into the grass ahead of the stick that hit it. Three girls, their long braids flying, raced for the rabbit. One of them found it in the tall grass and held it up as a trophy. The hunter smiled at the girl and told her she might keep the rabbit—as was the custom on a communal hunt. The girl kept it, but the next day, after she had cooked it, she would invite the hunter who had killed it to come to her house for a feast.

Young Hawk was so busy watching that he almost missed a jack rabbit lying still in the grass nearby, its long ears flattened against its head. Before it could move, he hit it with his stick and held it up for the boys to admire. It was a large,

heavy animal. He was sorry that the rabbit had been so near him, for he would have liked to race a girl for it. It seemed more fun that way.

The girls returned to their posts, moving cautiously in the grass. Suddenly one of them stepped back and the others who were behind her jumped out of the way. The boys were curious and came over to see what had frightened the girls. A snake was crawling through the grass, its red, yellow, and black rings shining in the sun. It was as unhurried as though it had the field all to itself. The

youngsters stepped back and watched the snake's progress, making no attempt to interfere with it. Snakes, they believed, had a strong power for bringing rain. No one wanted to hurt a snake for fear of making the snake spirits angry, for then they would not bring rain to the pueblos. The snake crawled away, zigzagging through the rabbit brush, till only the movement of the blades of grass showed the path it took. Soon even the grass was still.

"Look what I have," a girl shouted boastfully.

Young Hawk had dropped his rabbit as he watched the snake, and now one of the smaller girls had picked it up. He was glad it had worked out this way, for now the girl would share with him the lunch in her bulging bag and tomorrow he could go to her house to enjoy the meat she would cook. But he was anxious to hide his pleasure from his friends so they would not tease him about it later. He pretended to grab his rabbit and was glad that the girl was quicker. She jumped away from him, holding the rabbit behind her back.

The scouts had chosen excellent hunting grounds. Jack rabbits kept popping out of the grass all over the field. Men hurled their sticks again and again, throwing them once more as soon as they were recovered. By this time the sun was high overhead, and everyone welcomed the warmth.

The commotion and excitement continued. There was much laughter as a man reached the rabbit he had killed almost at the same time as

the woman next to him, and the man teased her
by refusing to give her the rabbit. The two tugged
at the rabbit and rolled in the grass, laughing.

Soon it was time for the midday meal and the
people formed small groups and circles. The
women and girls opened the bags and baskets they
had brought. They offered to share the corn-meal
cakes they had baked the night before and their
pieces of boiled rabbit meat with the men whose

rabbits they had picked up. Families ate slowly, enjoying the sunshine and the clear skies overhead.

A road runner, frightened out of the grass, suddenly ran past a group of hunters, mincing swiftly across the plain, raising its tall crest and swinging its long, graceful tail.

"It is strange that bird does not like to fly," one of the boys said, watching the road runner. "Yet it has wings. It seems to like staying on the ground. I wish I could fly. I would never walk."

"I wouldn't either," another boy agreed.

"I wonder whether men will ever learn to fly," the first boy said.

"Perhaps one day we will," Young Hawk replied. "The spirits fly. They could come and teach us. I would like to fly from one end of the earth to the other and see everything."

"Like the eagle up above," the first boy said, looking up.

Overhead an eagle was soaring high and everyone looked upward, watching it.

"What is that mighty one after?" a little girl asked.

"He is a hunter," her father said. "Let us see what he is after."

The eagle was now circling almost over the heads of the seated people. It dived and was up in the air instantly, carrying in its sharp talons a struggling jack rabbit. The eagle flew higher toward the cliffs.

"Now he, the mighty hunter, has his share of rabbit meat too," the little girl said. "He has a nest and young up there."

After the noonday rest, the hunt went on through the afternoon. Every woman and girl had a rabbit or two in her hands. By late afternoon all the rabbits in that hunting ground had either been killed or frightened away.

The sun was getting low in the sky and its slanting rays bathed the cliffs and mesas and valley in golden browns, blues, and deep greens. The people's faces, too, glowed coppery in the setting sun.

"It is time to return," said Young Hawk's father, and the people picked up the rabbits to carry them home.

The sunset never failed to fill the Indians with awe. In that land of colors no sunset was like another. Now everyone fell silent. The sky was a deep blue, and the scattered white clouds in it were burning red. The cliffs turned purple as the sun disappeared. The sagebrush, pale in the twilight, smelled stronger than ever.

"The Creator loves this earth and paints it anew at each sunrise and at each sunset," Young Hawk's father said to him. "He loves us, too, because he gave us this earth to live in."

The first stars began to appear and soon the sky was filled with stars. Young Hawk recalled the story of the stars Grandmother had told him when he was a little boy.

Before the first people came to live on the Rio Grande, they lived in a place known in legend as the White House. When all the people left the White House and started for the Rio Grande, a little girl was left behind.

Mother Earth called to her and gave her a large, white bag. Mother Earth said, "Do not untie the bag, little daughter. Keep it tied till you reach your pueblo and give the bag to your chief."

The girl started. She did not know what she was carrying. The bag was not heavy, but it was filled with something and the girl became curious. After a while she stopped, put the bag down, and loosened the knot. A few things flew out and scattered into the sky. The little girl tried to catch them, but they flew up so fast she could not. She tried to tie the knot again and could not. The things kept flying out till the bag hung limp and empty in her hands, and the sky was filled with glittering, twinkling stars.

Mother Earth had intended to name all the stars, but now that they were scattered it was impossible to name them. A few, like the Big Dipper, had already been named. But the others were

still unnamed, and so they remain to this day.
"Some day," Grandmother had said, "Mother
Earth will call the stars back and sort them out
and give them names. Then we will know them
all by name."

In the distance rose the shadow of their mesa.
In the dark no one would have guessed that its
top held fifty or more adobe homes. The small
doorways lighted by the fires burning in the fire-
pits acted like tiny beacons, cheering the youngsters and the adults as well. Each was sure that
the light he saw was in his home and that a warm
evening meal, prepared by the old folks, was waiting. The boys and girls forgot their weariness.
Shouting and laughing, they raced up the mesa
toward their beloved pueblo.

4

CRAFTS

SINCE the people in every pueblo household made their own tools, utensils, clothing, and ornaments, everyone worked hard to produce the things needed in everyday life. Men and women, boys and girls, were seldom idle. Whether they were at home or visiting a neighbor or in the kivas, they were busy weaving cloth, scraping tools, chipping arrowheads, making pottery, plaiting baskets and mats.

The River Indians were fortunate, because they grew much of their food and did not have to worry about finding it. They were usually able to stay in one place throughout their lives. They had time to develop skills in their crafts and new ways of doing things. Both men and women spent much time at home with their families and taught the boys and girls the skills they needed to know.

They were always on the lookout for things that might be useful for the household. While playing on the riverbank, Young Hawk and his friends often picked up stones and pieces of bone. A curved pebble might be just what Mother needed for a polishing stone when she was making pottery. A heavier stone that fitted her hand, she could use for pounding yucca leaves to make a mat or basket.

In those days all the tools were made of stone, bone, or wood. Men and boys looked for pieces of quartz, obsidian, and chert, which they used to flake arrowheads and to make their stone knives. A chunk of basalt might be made into a hammerstone or chipped and sharpened into a stone ax. On their walks, men marked saplings that would be cut later to make bows and arrow shafts, hoe handles, and digging sticks.

Young Hawk's uncle was an excellent arrow maker and he had promised the boy that he would

show him how to make a bow and arrow. Young
Hawk was delighted when one day Uncle called
him over to where he sat working outside his

house. Beside him on a mat were several hammerstones, a large sandstone slab, a basketful of as-
sorted rocks, and a pile of twigs and saplings he
had cut in the spring.

Uncle began to work on the bow first. He had
cut an oak sapling about an arm and a half long.
The sapling had a slight curve to it. Uncle scraped

it with a stone knife, shaping it so it was thickest at the middle and tapered at both ends. At each end Uncle cut a notch to hold the bowstring. He rubbed the bow on the sandstone to make it smooth. Then he held the bow over hot ashes, to steam and soften it so that it would become pliable. Some men preferred a straight bow, which they would bend to a curve with the bow-string. This gave the bow a stronger pull.

Uncle made the bowstring of sinew from a deer's leg. Several strands of sinew were stripped off and allowed to soak. When they were soft, Uncle rolled and twisted them on his thigh, just as he did when he spun thread of cotton or yucca fiber. He was careful to knot one end of the bow-string with a half hitch, for the string would always have to be loosened when the bow was not in use. Otherwise, the continuous pull on the bow-string would stretch it and it would lose its spring. The men usually carried an extra bowstring in their quiver, in case the one on the bow should break.

Uncle made arrow shafts out of small straight branches of sumac or oak. Some arrow shafts were as long as a man's arm, some shorter. Young Hawk helped scrape the bark of the arrow shafts on the sandstone slab. He smoothed and evened the shafts by rubbing them with a rough stone. To straighten the shafts, Uncle steamed them over the fire till they were pliable, then pushed them through a piece of horn. Some men scraped the arrow shafts to a point at one end. Such arrows, shot from a strong bow, did not tear the skin of the animals hit by them.

Next Uncle went to work making arrowheads. He used pieces of flint and obsidian which he had soaked in water. With a blow from a hammer-stone he chipped off a large piece. Pressing the point of an antler against it, he flaked bits off the edges till he had shaped an arrowhead.

He split the arrow shaft with a stone knife, pushed the arrow point into the slit, and squeezed in a little piñon pine gum. While Young Hawk held the shaft, Uncle wrapped wet sinew around the split end. As the sinew dried, it shrank and held the arrowhead firmly in the shaft.

Wet sinew was also used to attach feathers to the arrow shaft. First Uncle split several feathers in the middle and glued three to the shaft with piñon gum. Then he wrapped wet sinew around them.

Every day while Uncle worked with Young Hawk at his side, neighbors stopped by for a chat. On the second day, while Uncle was rolling the sinew for the bowstring, an old man came over. He had made gourd rattles for the winter ceremonials, and Young Hawk was interested in seeing them. Father made many rattles too, and Young Hawk always helped him. The Indians liked to shake rattles while dancing. The sound added to their enjoyment of the ceremony.

The old man had found several large gourds, some round and some egg-shaped. These grew wild in the meadows. He had cut two openings in the sides of each gourd and had put them away till the insides dried. After a few days he poured sharp pebbles into each gourd and shook it. The pebbles loosened the drying seeds and pulp and they fell out when he shook the gourd.

Again the old man let the gourds dry for a few days, but this time he filled them with dry sand and plugged up the holes with pieces of wood. The sand kept the gourds from losing their shape while they were drying. When the gourds were thoroughly dry, the man put a few smooth, rounded pebbles into each one and pushed in a piece of wood for a handle. The smooth pebbles made the right sound as he shook each rattle for Young Hawk and Uncle. Later, in the kiva, the old man planned to paint designs on the rattles. Then they would be ready for the ceremonies.

The River Indians also liked the sound of rattles made from deer and antelope hoofs. The men tied the hoofs to their ankles, knees, or belts. These clicked in rhythm as they danced.

The notched stick was another noisemaker used during ceremonials. There were usually two or three of them at every ceremony. These were easy to make. A sapling was scraped and flattened on one side. On the other side, a man cut ridges with his stone knife. During a ceremony he put one end of the notched stick on the ground and held the other end straight up. With his other hand he scraped a short stick up and down the ridges.

In the old days drums were made mostly from pots partly filled with water and covered with buffalo skin. The tough buffalo hide made the best drumhead. The skin was soaked and stretched over the mouth of the pot while it was still wet and, as it dried, the skin shrank and made a taut drumhead. Later men learned to make drums of short hollowed cottonwood logs with tight skin covers over both ends. This made a better drum than one made of pottery, since it was not as apt to be cracked or broken.

Ever since the River Indians could remember, they had treasured turquoise for ornaments. At first, although turquoise is a soft stone, they did not try to drill holes in it to make beads. Instead, they chipped the turquoise and glued these chips with piñon gum to pieces of wood, shell, and bone, making very attractive pendants. Later they learned to use a drill.

Another neighbor joined Uncle and Young Hawk on the third day, bringing with him a new drill. As Young Hawk watched, he twirled the drill and bored a hole in a piece of turquoise. It took him a long time to make one turquoise bead.

Uncle told Young Hawk he was planning to make such a drill too. He showed the neighbor a basket full of shells he had traded with an Indian from the South. "The shells will make a beautiful necklace for my son's wife," Uncle said to Young Hawk.

Uncle's oldest son would soon be married. He was weaving the white wedding robe, or *manta*, for the bride and also the belt she would wear. Several of his relatives were helping him. In the low moist places by the Rio Grande the Indians raised small patches of cotton. They dried the cotton plants and pulled out the fluff by hand.

During the long winter evenings a family worked together pulling out the seeds or beating them out with sticks. Spinning cotton thread took a long time. This work was done by the men with a spindle, which was rolled up and down the leg and thigh.

When a man had spun enough thread, he set up a simple loom and began to weave. He made his own ceremonial kilts. He wove cloth for shirts, for his wife's skirts, and for breechcloths.

The women did the sewing and made the moccasins for the family, as well as the baskets and mats. At one time baskets were very important to these Indians. That was before they had perfected the art of making pottery. But even after the women learned to make pots and bowls, they still needed baskets and mats. Women and girls were always gathering yucca leaves to make these things. They used sumac, barberry, and rabbit brush to make the large burden baskets in which the men carried their harvests from the cornfields

and trade goods on their trading trips from pueblo to pueblo.

To make a yucca basket, a woman first plaited a yucca mat. Then she dampened it till it became soft. She made a ring out of a sumac stem and twisted the ends of the mat over the ring, sewing the basket together with strands of split yucca. The women had no needles. Instead, they used a bone awl. These yucca baskets are still used today in every pueblo household.

Basket and mat making went on all the time in every household. These did not take as much effort as pottery making, which required great skill. There is a legend the River Indians like to tell about how they first learned to make pottery.

"Once long ago," their legend says, "we did not have pots and we did not know how to make them. People cooked their food in the ground, in pits they had scooped out. It took a whole day to prepare a meal. So Mother Earth, the mother of all our people, took pity on us.

" 'The people must have pots in which to cook and pots in which to carry water,' Mother Earth said. She sent her old father and mother down to earth to teach the people how to make pots out of clay. The old couple came to the River pueblos —Old Clay Woman and Old Clay Man. Both wore masks of white clay with large beautiful eyes and with many designs on them. Old Clay Woman wore a white *manta* and a wide white belt. Old Clay Man wore a brown buckskin kilt. He carried a stick and a burden basket full of clay on his back.

"When they entered the pueblo, all the people came out to see the beautiful strangers: the old man with his stick and basket, the old woman wearing her snow-white *manta* and belt.

"Old Clay Woman sat down in the plaza in the center of the pueblo. She took the clay out of the basket and mixed it with water. She mixed the clay well and kneaded it and wrapped it in her *manta*. After a while she began to roll the clay into long sausagelike rolls. She shaped a base from a lump of clay and began to coil the long rolls of clay around it to make the walls of a pot. The people had never seen a clay pot before and they were delighted to see something in which they could cook their stews and carry water from the Rio Grande.

"While Old Clay Woman worked, Old Clay Man, holding spruce twigs and prayer sticks, was doing a dance so the spirits would help Old Clay Woman in her work.

"Old Clay Woman made a large pot. She set it down to dry in the sun just as Old Clay Man was finishing his dance. As he stepped back, he carelessly kicked the pot with his heel and it broke into many pieces. Angered, Old Clay Woman picked up the old man's stick and began to chase him. All the people thought this very funny and they laughed and shouted. Some advised the old woman how to catch her husband. Others told the old man where to run to escape. Old Clay Woman finally caught her husband and they made up their quarrel. Old Clay Man picked up the pieces of pottery and Old Clay Woman made them into a clay ball again.

"Old Clay Man took the lump of clay and gave some to every woman in the pueblo. Each woman sat down and began to roll the clay and make a pot just as Old Clay Woman had made hers. And so the women learned to make pottery. At first the pots were plain, but later each woman learned to make designs on her pots with brushes of twigs and black and red paint."

Each pueblo had its own clay pits where generation after generation of women dug the clay for pots. Each woman went to the clay pits several times a year. As she bent down to scoop up the clay, she always prayed to Mother Earth, thanking her for the clay and asking her help in making beautiful pots. The women also had special places where they dug for sand. The clay had to be mixed with sand to make good pots.

In her free time Young Hawk's mother always took the lumps of moist clay she kept in the storeroom and reworked them. After grinding the clay on a *metate* to make it soft and fine, she picked out all the pebbles and coarse vegetable matter. Then she added sand to the clay, or crushed volcanic rock. From long practice she knew just the right amount to add so her pots would not blister or form air bubbles.

Mother used an old bowl as a base. Into it she patted a lump of clay. She rolled the clay into long sausages and coiled them around the clay

base, building up the walls of the pot. These walls were straight at first. Having built up the walls, Mother let the pot dry for a while, usually starting to work on another pot. When the first dried sufficiently, Mother began to press gently and evenly with wet hands on the walls, to curve them to the desired shape.

Then the pot had to dry again in the shade. Pots had to be dried slowly or they would crack. Mother smoothed and scraped the dried pots with a piece of gourd rind, so the walls would be of even thickness. If the pot was to be used for cooking, she set it aside for firing. If she planned to use a pot or bowl for serving food, Mother covered it with a special slip, a mixture of red or white clay and water. With a piece of buckskin she put a coating of the slip on the pot, sometimes adding a second and even a third coat.

Now it was time to rub in the slip. Mother took a smooth pebble and began to polish the pot with it. After much rubbing, the pot shone as though it had been covered with a thick coat of wax.

The last step before firing was painting designs on the pot. The River Indian women used feather designs, triangles, squares, or broken lines. The ends of twigs or yucca leaves made good brushes. The paints were made by mixing earth colors with water or boiling the stems of plants.

Holding the pot in her lap, Mother patiently drew a design on it and let it dry. The design on each pot and bowl was a little different from all the others. Now the pot was ready for firing.

Early in the morning, Mother made a small

fire in a fire pit outside the house. She put the pots into the center of the pit and placed firewood all around the pit. She put pieces of bark and thin slabs of stone around the pots to make sure the flames never touched them while they were being fired. In this way she avoided having black smudges or "fire clouds" on her pottery.

With a small fire and no wind, the pots warmed up gradually and evenly. Then Mother added wood so the pots would really bake through and through. When they had baked long enough, she let the fire go out and took the pots out of the pit and let them cool slowly.

With plenty of pots, baskets, and a full store-room, a River Indian household could look forward to many comfortable months ahead.

5

CEREMONIES AND DANCES

THE Indians of Kishtaya and other pueblos were busy with farming, hunting, and their household tasks during spring, summer, and fall. But, in spite of all this work, the River Indian devoted much of the time to his religion. Many of the ancient religious ceremonies and dances are still observed by these River Indians today.

Each man owned various sacred possessions, some of which were kept in his own home. Things used in the many festivals were kept in the back of the living room or in the small storage room. The costumes worn at these dances, the masks, the turkey and eagle feathers worn in the hair, the sticks with feathers tied to them called prayer sticks, the drums, rattles, and sacred bundles were all carefully stored. The old men of the household were responsible for these ceremonial things. They believed that the costumes, the feathers, and the masks used in ceremonies were sacred and had to be treated with special attention. From time to time the old men and the medicine men sprinkled corn meal and pollen over them. They prayed and chanted as they unfolded and aired the costumes. They believed that the prayers and chants, the corn meal and the pollen, fed the sacred objects and helped renew their power.

The medicine men owned sacred things of

their own that held special powers. These were feathers, claws of animals or birds, pieces of fur, birds' heads and beaks. The owner wrapped these things carefully in skins, and such a package was called a sacred bundle. From time to time the owner of a sacred bundle unwrapped it and sprinkled corn meal over it to feed the spirits. Sacred, too, were the enemy scalps which some medicine men and warriors owned. These Indians believed that a scalp held a man's spirit and strength. Whoever carried a scalp in battle had double strength —his own and the strength and supernatural power of the enemy's scalp.

In every Rio Grande pueblo there were kivas, or ceremonial chambers. Some were round and some square. An opening in the ceiling was the kiva's only entrance and a ladder led from the opening to the floor. This ladder could be pulled in when the men were busy with important matters and did not want to be disturbed. The people in each pueblo were divided into two main groups: the Summer People and the Winter People. All the different societies in each pueblo belonged to one or the other of these two groups. The kiva of the Summer People was the Squash Kiva, and the Winter People's was the Turquoise Kiva. In these kivas each member had his own place. There he could keep his few tools—his rabbit stick, his bow and arrows, his small loom.

A person could belong to several societies, depending on the group into which he was born. A boy became a member by being initiated into a society to which his relatives belonged. A girl was initiated into a woman's society to which her relatives belonged. A boy had to fast for a few days and do special tasks before his initiation. His relatives gave gifts of food to the society when the boy was accepted.

When a young man inherited a sacred bundle, he brought it with him to his kiva and kept it there. A man who took a scalp in war usually brought it for safekeeping to the ceremonial room of the Warriors' Society. The warrior and the scalp taken in war were received with much ceremony. If the man was not already a member of the Warriors' Society, he was immediately invited to join. This was a great honor.

Besides the Warriors' Society, there were other societies in each pueblo. There was always the society of the Koshare (Ko-sha-ray), a society which is still important to these Indians. The Koshare represented the spirits of ancestors who begged the gods for good things for the pueblo people. The Koshare clowned and danced at festivals to make people laugh. If anyone became angry with a Koshare, it was as though that person were angry with the spirits of his ancestors— and of course that would offend them. The Koshare held their own dance each spring, but joined in the festivities of other societies as well.

Next in importance to the Warriors' Society and the Koshare was the Hunters' Society. Its members took charge of the village rabbit hunts and other hunting activities, and the Warriors and Koshare helped them.

At their dances and festivals all societies honored the spirits. In each ceremonial house and kiva there was always a special place called the altar, where the sacred objects were kept. A path-

way of sacred meal led from the altar to the door of the kiva so the spirits might enter. Several ceremonial bowls filled with corn meal, prayer sticks, sacred bundles, and carved figures of bird and animal spirits were placed at the altar.

The supernatural powers and spirits in which

these Indians believed in ancient times, and in which some of them still believe today, are called kachinas. Once long ago, according to legend, the kachinas often came from their world to visit the pueblos. Now they come only at certain times to teach the men, who do the kachina dances at ceremonies, the right steps and how to make the masks these kachina dancers wear. When a kachina dancer wears such a mask at a ceremony, the kachina spirits come and give him some of their supernatural powers with which to help the people. The kachinas are supposed to be good spirits, bringing health, rain, plentiful crops, and happiness.

In all the pueblos, men also carve wooden dolls which they call kachinas. The details of these kachina dolls—their dress, feathers, color, and posture—were determined in ancient times and handed down from one generation to the next. Some of them, for example, are double-headed. Men taught their children and grandchildren to carve kachinas. All the details had to be correct;

otherwise the kachina spirit would be offended.

There were several medicine societies in each pueblo. The important medicine societies fought witches. The less important ones, such as the Snakes and the Ants, cured various ailments, especially those caused by snake bite and by ants. The pueblo people believed that ants got inside a person's body and made him sick. It was the duty of the members of the Ants Society to suck the ant out of the victim's body during a special curing ceremony.

The fighting of ailments caused by witches was even more important. A person who could harm another by supernatural power was believed to be a witch. The witch could be a man or a woman. He could wish sickness for his enemy and the person sickened. He might shoot broken glass, thorns, or pebbles into an enemy's body to make him sick. He worked secretly, of course, and no one in the pueblos liked even to speak of witchcraft. The curing could be done only by members of one of the medicine societies. The members held a dance and sucked out the object that caused the sickness. In many cases the victim recovered. In some, however, he died. If the medicine man thought the witch had stolen the victim's heart, he had to go out and bring it back. The medicine man brought back a round bundle supposed to hold the victim's heart. He opened the bundle, took out a kernel of corn which represented the heart, and then told the victim to swallow the kernel of corn. In that way the victim got his heart back and was cured. Many of these beliefs and customs about witchcraft still exist today in the River pueblos.

One of the most important religious festivals was the Green Corn Dance. By August the cornfields of Kishtaya were at their best. In each field, row upon row, leafy green cornstalks were bending with the weight of the filling ears. Close by were the rows of beans and spreading squash with their large yellow blossoms.

In August the men paused in their work for a few days to prepare for their Green Corn Dance.

Like the other dances and ceremonials, this was a thanksgiving to the spirits for their fine fields. Prayers for more rain would be offered, so the crops would ripen without mishap.

All the details of the Green Corn Dance are not known to us. The Indians have not told outsiders exactly what takes place during the dance, either in or out of their kivas. The preparations and prayers for the dance began in the kivas. On the first day of the dance the Koshare came out of the kivas and danced all around the pueblo. Since a Koshare represented the spirit of an ancestor, he painted designs on his body with gray or brown earth colors. He matted his hair with clay and tied it in tufts with cornhusks. He dyed his breechcloth black and tied it with a dry rabbitskin thong. He also tied thongs of rabbitskin about his ankles. In his hands he carried spruce branches.

After the Koshare completed their circling about Kishtaya, they held a council in the plaza. Runners were immediately sent out to all four

points of the compass. These runners were scouts
sent out to see whether any enemy was approaching to raid the harvest. The Navaho from the
west, the Apache and Comanche from the east,
often tried to raid the fields of Kishtaya.

When the runners returned, the warriors
joined the Koshare and took a special drink made
of herbs to make them vomit. The Indians believed this vomiting purified the warriors for the
coming battle with the raiders, so the spirits
would favor them. The Koshare and the members of the Warriors' Society then went down into
the kivas. No outsider has yet found out exactly
what took place there. We know that they prayed
and danced.

A tall pole, twice the height of a man, was
stuck in the roof of each kiva. Tied to this standard were brilliant feathers, a foxskin, and a man's
wide kilt. While these standards were up, everyone in Kishtaya knew that ceremonies were going
on inside the kivas. As soon as the standards were
taken down, it meant that the Koshare, the war-

riors, and the medicine men were about to come out.

Everyone got ready now to join in the dance. The women put on their best ornaments and combed their hair. Each one carried evergreen twigs in her hands.

The men wore breechcloths and kilts of white buckskin and a broad belt with dangling streamers. Each man had tied a foxskin at the back of

his breechcloth and had placed bright feathers in
his long hair. The men wore deer-hoof rattles
on their belts and ankles. They carried turtle-shell
and gourd rattles in their hands.

The men and boys formed in single file. The
women and girls formed another line. Men and
women danced for the rest of the day to the sound
of drums and rattles, the noises made by notched
sticks, and a chorus of men's voices. The standards were carried by medicine men, who led the
files of dancers. As the dancers moved, the standard waved over them and the Koshare danced in
between the files of the dancers. No one paid any
attention to the Koshare, because they were supposed to be invisible, but each dancer made sure
that during the day he or she passed at least four
times under the sacred standard. This, they believed, would insure that each of them would
get an ample harvest.

At Kishtaya the gathering in of the harvest
was also a time of ceremonies. The men harvested
their corn in late September or early October,

pulling off the ears of corn by hand and loading them into large burden baskets. Then the corn was carried up to the village. The whole pueblo was cleaned for this occasion. They did this to welcome the corn, as they welcomed honored guests to Kishtaya. They knew the corn spirit would be glad to be so honored and would continue to come to them in abundant harvests.

Important ceremonies and dances were held at the end of the year. The men from the different societies planned these ceremonies and set the days for them. One of the most important was the buffalo dance. Although it was called a buffalo dance, there were usually antelope, deer, elk, and mountain-sheep dancers in it besides the buffalo dancers. These dancers made their different costumes and practiced their dances in the ceremonial houses and the kivas. The buffalo dancers wore the heads of real buffaloes with the horns and hair. When not in use, the heads were kept in a ceremonial house and were cared for by a

special priest, as were the deer, the antelope, and the mountain-sheep heads and costumes.

In the buffalo dance, only the buffalo dancers stood erect and danced erect. The other animal dancers bent over to imitate the actions of other animals. Some of them held sticks in their hands to make walking and dancing in this position easier.

It took several weeks to prepare for the buffalo dance. The dancers practiced so they could imitate the movements of their animals perfectly. Although the dancers tried to copy the costumes usually worn for these occasions, each added a little out of his own imagination, and so the costumes were rich in detail.

On the morning of the buffalo dance, everyone in Kishtaya waited at home until a messenger came to announce that the dance was being held. Then the people lined up about the plaza to wait for the dancers to enter. Two men wearing buffalo heads always led the dance. They came into the plaza first and a woman danced between them.

She was supposed to be the mother of all the game animals. The woman wore a beautiful white *manta*, white moccasins and leggings. People greeted the dancers by sprinkling them with corn meal.

The deer and antelope dancers followed. They danced around and around in a circle, the buffaloes dancing erect, the other animals on all fours, turning their huge heads from side to side, skipping and hopping. The dance lasted all morning. At noon the dancers left the plaza and the audience, too, went away to eat and rest. They returned in the afternoon, and the dancers came soon after and danced for the rest of the afternoon.

Toward the end of the day, the War Chief cried out that they were going to have a hunt and all the dancers began to run, with the people chasing after them. A few of the animals were caught and held. These dancers were treated as though they were game that had been killed. As in a rabbit hunt, the women rushed up to touch them.

The men with them lifted the animals and carried them to the homes of the women who had touched them.

There the animal dancers were treated with the same ceremony that a real animal killed in the hunt received. The deer, for instance, was covered with a white *manta*. Then the man of the household blew tobacco smoke over the *manta* and removed it. The deer dancer got up, and the men ordered him to go back to the land of the spirits and see to it that the man of the house and his sons and nephews had good luck in getting deer when they hunted. This the spirit deer promised, as he left the house with small gifts of food and feathers given him by the family.

These year-end dances were repeated during the next three days. In the evenings after the ceremonies, all the people feasted and danced.

6

TRADING

FLARES had been burning all night in every home at Kishtaya, for the Comanche were coming to trade. Men and women with robes thrown over their shoulders flitted back and forth and up and down the ladders on errands. Long after the children were sound asleep, their mothers knelt over the grinding stones. In some homes, an older child, a grandfather, or a grandmother remained to watch the house while the mother and father went to a neighbor's house to grind corn. When there was a lot of corn to grind, the women of Kishtaya liked to grind it together.

At the War Chief's house, three women were kneeling in front of three grinding stones. Two other women were busy shelling corn of different colors into baskets. Carefully counting the ears, each woman made sure that she put in an equal share. When the corn was ground into flour, she would get the same amount of corn meal as the others.

The husbands sat near the fire. The War Chief put a neatly cut package of cornhusks before them and a small bag of tobacco. Whenever men gathered together they liked to start the evening with a smoke.

Men raised little patches of tobacco in their fields. In the fall, they dried the tobacco leaves, crushed them, and stored them in small bags. They also set aside the finer cornhusks to be used in rolling cigarettes. This native tobacco was very strong and a man could smoke only one or two cigarettes in an evening. If he smoked more he would have a headache the following morning. So these Indians did not smoke much; neither did they usually smoke when they were alone. Boys did not smoke at all; neither did the women. Only after a young man had killed a deer, an antelope, a jack rabbit, and a coyote was he considered worthy to smoke with the men. An unmarried man never smoked with his elders. If any boy or young man smoked before he was proved worthy, he was carried to the river and given a thorough ducking in the presence of the entire pueblo. Not many youngsters wanted to be shamed in this way.

Tobacco was sacred. A messenger going from pueblo to pueblo among the River Indians usually carried a small bag of tobacco with him. After he had delivered the message to a chief, he offered the bag of tobacco. In accepting a gift of tobacco, the chief agreed to the message. If he refused the tobacco, it meant that he did not wish to accept the message.

These Indians also used tobacco as medicine. If anyone had a toothache, the medicine man put a bit of tobacco into the cavity to relieve the pain. To cure a cold, a person put some tobacco in his nostrils. When a woman was having severe pains giving birth to a child, tobacco was mixed

with herbs and water and given to her to drink
to relieve the pain.

Now the War Chief invited the men, saying,
as the host always did at this time, "Come and sit

down. Smoke. It will rain very much." He and
the others believed that tobacco smoke was like
clouds that bring rain.

Each man took a piece of cornhusk, shook some
tobacco into it, and rolled the husk into a tube.
He put it into his mouth and the youngest of the

men picked up an ember in a piece of bark and each man lit his cigarette. Following the ceremony set by custom, each man took a puff and blew it first in one direction; then he took another puff and blew it in another direction. Six puffs covered all six directions: east, west, north, south, up, and down.

The strong tobacco burned their throats. They spat into the fire and coughed loudly. Young Hawk watched them, knowing that one day when he was older he would have to do the same. None of the men seemed to enjoy it.

After they finished smoking, one man placed before him the small drum he had brought with him and began to beat it with his hands. He had hollowed it out of a cottonwood log with a sharpened stone knife. Next he had covered the top and bottom with two pieces of rawhide which his wife had tanned. The rawhide had been well soaked before he put it on the hollow log and pulled the ends taut with thongs of buckskin running from top to bottom. As the rawhide dried, it shrank and made tightly fitting heads. Now he beat the drum and the men began to sing. This was a tune the men always sang while the women ground corn into meal. The women found that the rhythmical beat of the drum and the men's singing helped while away the long hours at the *metates*. When the men stopped singing, the women resumed their talk about their households and about pueblo matters.

The women were making parched corn meal. This meal did not spoil as quickly as unparched meal, and it was much in demand in trading. First a woman crushed the kernels on her coarse grinding stone. As she finished a few handfuls of meal, another woman took the basket of coarse meal to the fire. The baking stone had been heated. She carefully spread the corn meal on it for a minute and then scooped it into another basket. A third woman, kneeling before another *metate*, took the basket with the parched corn and ground it some more. After she finished, the meal was given a final parching before it was ground even finer on a third *metate*. The parched meal was a golden brown.

"This will bring us several buffalo robes in trade," Young Hawk's mother said. "We need the robes. I cut down an old buffalo robe of my husband's for Young Hawk two winters ago and now he is too big for it. I must get a new robe for my husband. Then I will trim down and fix the worn places on his old robe and let Young Hawk have it."

"Older Son has enough of his own things for trading with the Comanche when they come here," a neighbor said. "He has been trapping and shooting birds, so now he has plenty of feathers for trading. He and my brother have shot many wild turkeys, and you know how the Comanche value feathers."

"I've saved and dried the squash we raised. Those Indians like bundles of squash. Maybe I'll get some dried buffalo meat in trade," said the third neighbor hopefully.

"My wife always talks about trading and tells me just how to trade," one of the men said as he overheard the women's conversation. "But when the Comanche come, she is so shy, like all women, that she never says a word to them."

"It is better for our women not to have much to say to these wanderers of the plains," the War Chief said. "They are very different from us. They may try to steal from us and we must watch them. But we must make sure they do not notice it. When people come to trade, it is not good to start fighting or to make them suspicious."

It was dawn when the women finished grinding corn. Every basket, pot, and buckskin bag in the households at Kishtaya was full of corn meal; bundles of dried squash; beans, dried and ground; dried berries; cherries; and wild plants.

In the War Chief's house, three women were now busy making wafer bread. The others had also gone home to cook and bake.

The women did not lie down to rest that night. At dawn each spread a clean yucca mat in front of her house and placed on it the things she wanted to trade: corn cakes, wafer bread, a pair of buckskin moccasins, several bundles of dried squash.

One woman put on her mat a rabbitskin blanket which her youngest child had outgrown. But that did not wait for the coming of the Comanche. A woman from across the plaza passed by with her water jug on her head and saw the neat blanket. She was back in short order, with a covered basket of yellow wafer bread.

"Neighbor," she said, "I have made this wafer bread for you. I see that you have no bread of this color. You may trade it for something good with the Comanche." All the time she was speaking she did not take her eyes off the rabbitskin blanket. The owner knew that the wafer bread would be more desirable to the Comanche than a rabbitskin blanket, since they had enough buffalo robes to keep them warm. She took the wafer bread and picked up the blanket and gave it to the woman.

Both women smiled at each other. Neighbors

exchanged gifts. They did not trade. Sometimes a woman was not willing to part with a pot or basket her neighbor wanted very much, but by means of continuous gifts the neighbor eventually had her way and got the pot or basket. The same held true with things a man wanted. Young Hawk always recalled with disappointment the quiverful of arrows that had belonged to his uncle. Uncle was older now and did not do as much deer hunting as he used to do. Young Hawk had been sure that he would get these arrows. But one of the men wanted Uncle's bow and the arrows, too. He was forever giving gifts to Uncle's wife, buckskins for a pair of moccasins or a few ears of corn from his field. He even carried firewood for her. One day he brought a mountain lion's skin and gave it to Uncle. That closed the deal. There was nothing left for Uncle to do but give the man his bow, the quiver, and all his arrows.

By the time the sun was up, each woman had finished arranging the things she wanted to trade

Now she retired indoors to dress in her best skirt and blanket and to comb her hair.

Each woman had combed her husband's long hair earlier and had fixed it with a knot in the back and a band tied around his head. The men were sitting in little groups in the plaza. They, too, had things to trade. Some wore turquoise pendants, shell necklaces, and several pairs of earrings; others carried several bows and quivers loaded with arrows. Some had little bags of flaked arrowheads, stone knives, and hammerstones. The wandering Comanche were always on the go. They did not have enough time to sit and make all these things and were glad to trade for them. Many of the men had little bags of tobacco and packets of cornhusks which they also wanted to trade.

The War Chief asked Young Hawk to stay with Mother and speak for her. He had to be free to go about the pueblo with the Pueblo Chief to greet the men who came to trade. He also had to watch the trading and keep things in hand. A man might get into an argument with a Comanche and it might lead to a fight and start a war. This had happened in other villages on the Rio Grande when wandering Indians from the plains and mountains had come to trade. It would not do to have it happen here and spoil the day's trading.

When the War Chief said to Young Hawk, "Speak for your mother," he did not really mean *speak*, since the Comanche had an entirely different language and Young Hawk spoke only his own. These Indians used sign language, and Young Hawk had learned enough of it to be able to "speak" it. His mother, on the other hand, did not know sign language at all.

A lookout posted on the edge of the mesa motioned to the men. All the boys immediately rushed over to get a good look at the Comanche.

About two dozen Comanche men were approaching in the valley below. They trotted briskly in single file, and the boys craned over the top of the mesa, watching them. From that distance they looked small. But as they started up the narrow path that led to Kishtaya, the boys saw that most of the men were taller than their fathers. Their hair, parted in the middle, was arranged in two long braids. Most of them had put some paint on their faces, and all wore one or two eagle feathers. "Those feathers must have come from trading with our pueblos," a boy said. "They always want to trade for eagle feathers."

The Comanche wore buckskin leggings and shirts. Each carried a heavy pack on his shoulders. "They have enough to trade," Young Hawk's best friend shouted to him.

The boys now stepped back and let the Pueblo Chief and the War Chief step forward with three dozen men. If the Comanche had any mischief in mind, they could see at a glance that they were outnumbered.

As the first Comanche came up the narrow path, he stopped and waited. The Pueblo Chief made a sign of welcome to him to come forward. He did so and his men lined up on both sides of

him and behind him. Now the Pueblo Chief of
Kishtaya spoke, using sign language.

"We welcome you in peace," he said. "You,
our brothers of the plains, are mighty hunters of
the buffalo. We have worked hard and our good
Mother Earth, the sun above, the clouds and
wind, have brought us good crops. Our women
have worked hard grinding corn and baking so
you will have enough to eat now to satisfy your
hunger after this long journey, and you will be
able to take back the good food of our lands to
your women and children."

As though at a given signal, the women came
out of their doorways with more corncakes, still
steaming hot, and baskets of wafer bread. They
placed on the mats pots full of corn dumplings.
As the Comanche scattered over the plaza, the
women dipped gourd spoons into the pots and
offered food to them.

The Comanche chief, led by the War Chief,
stopped in front of Young Hawk. Mother, too,
had made some corn dumplings. The round balls

of corn meal and berries were steaming hot. She offered a spoonful to the chief. He sat down on the mat in the doorway and began to eat the hot food.

Young Hawk eyed the Comanche chief suspiciously. The chief did not carry a pack. Is it possible that he came empty-handed, Young Hawk thought, and that Mother will not get the buffalo robe she wants? He looked around the plaza as the Comanche chief ate in silence, and he saw with envy that the other men had lowered their packs to the ground. The women's eyes were bright with curiosity, but good manners prevented anyone from asking to see what was inside a pack and even from looking at it too carefully.

The War Chief saw Young Hawk's disappointment and patted him on the back to reassure him.

The Comanche chief ate slowly, enjoying himself. Young Hawk saw that the Comanche was taking it all in and was keeping an eye on his men to see that they behaved. He, too, did not

want any trouble, especially since they were so outnumbered.

Having finished eating, the Comanche chief began to look over the food spread before him. He uncovered the basket of wafer bread. Young Hawk's mouth began to water, and he looked directly at the chief. The chief said something and two men with large packs came over. Young Hawk nearly jumped for joy. So these men carried the chief's load! What a lot of stuff he had brought!

Standing beside Mother, Young Hawk began to trade, pointing at the things his mother wanted in exchange for the bread, the sacks of parched corn, the packs of dried squash, the packets of cornhusks and bags of tobacco.

A neighbor now moved her baskets of corn and wafer bread to the War Chief's house. She was through with her trading, because the Comanche who had stopped in her doorway was more interested in feathers than in food and had quickly traded his one buffalo robe for two bundles of parrot and turkey feathers. The Comanche chief took a basket of wafer bread from her and Young Hawk now traded for the two women.

The Comanche who had finished their trading packed up the goods they had received and moved to the center of the plaza to talk and trade with the men.

One by one, as the mats before their homes were emptied, the women went indoors to look over their new possessions more carefully. The buffalo robes would be a great help during the winter. The buckskins would make many pairs of moccasins, and the good dried buffalo meat would make the corn mush tasty and give their children and husbands strength.

The Comanche chief, having finished his trading with the women, got up and joined his men in the plaza. He sat down near the War Chief. He had news to tell.

Far down to the south, the Comanche told the War Chief in sign language, new people were moving in. Men with queer pale faces were coming into Indian lands. They were riding on strange animals that looked like large dogs, and they had terrifying weapons that made loud noises.

The War Chief said he, too, had heard of such men. His father had said that when he was young several hundred palefaces came up from the south, but they did not stay in the River Indian country. They turned east and were never seen again. After a while the River Indians had forgotten the rumors about the palefaces dressed in shining clothing and riding on strange big animals. The news brought by the Comanche chief recalled those early worries. But it was no use alarming the women and children.

"Perhaps we should send scouts south to find out if this is true," the Pueblo Chief suggested.

The Comanche were shouldering their packs, ready to start back across the mountains to the plains.

"If the palefaces come in big numbers," the Comanche chief said in sign language, "do not fight them. They have sticks that blow fire. But if you can get any of those big animals, I will trade you many buffalo robes for each animal. They would be good for buffalo hunting."

7

CONQUEST AND RECONQUEST

THE War Chief and the Pueblo Chief of Kishtaya kept their secret and their worries about the coming of the palefaces to themselves. The cold winter months passed and spring came at last to Kishtaya. Again the men and boys left at dawn each day to clear the cornfields and get the irrigation ditches working. The women were busy cleaning up too, after the winter snowfalls and winds. They covered leaks in their roofs with a thick coat of mud. They scraped the earthen floor of their houses and swept the paths of the pueblo clean. Life and work went on again as they had for many centuries. The War Chief and the Pueblo Chief were glad they had not alarmed the people about the palefaces.

Then one day in late spring, the news came. A scout from a pueblo to the south ran breathless up the narrow path to Kishtaya and poured out his news to the alarmed people. The Kishtayans barely had time to call the men in from the fields when the valley below was filled with a large army of warriors. The people had never seen anything like it before. Most of the warriors rode large animals that were unknown to the Kishtayans. This was the first time they had ever seen horses. They kept pointing out to each other the wonders of this strange army. Some men were covered from head to foot with shining armor. From the distance a rider and horse looked like one strange large being. The Indians began to feel fear, for they knew they could not fight this tremendous army of invaders.

Suddenly the army came to a halt. A horseman in front shouted a command and waved a gleaming sword. This was followed by a boom and a cloud of smoke from a cannon. The boom of the cannon threw the Indians into a panic, as it was intended to do.

"We cannot fight these invaders with our bows and arrows," the War Chief said. And the men agreed. "Perhaps if we receive them in peace, we will have peace."

The chiefs of Kishtaya and the men lined up,

ready to receive the enemy. And that was how
Juan de Oñate, the Spanish explorer, came from
Mexico to Kishtaya in the spring of 1598.

Oñate did not stay long at the pueblo. Before
leaving, he ordered the Pueblo Chief to fill two
wagons with corn and beans. In vain the chief
protested. "The food we have will just last us till
the next harvest. If we give you any of our corn,
our women and children will starve."

In reply, the Spanish soldiers rushed into the

homes and began to carry out not only armfuls of corn but robes and buckskins as well, while other soldiers in the valley turned the cannon's mouth toward Kishtaya. It was no use trying to fight back. The women brought out their precious corn and loaded the wagons. Then the Spaniards moved on to the north.

Scouts from Kishtaya followed them and learned that they finally stopped at the village of Okeonwi, which was later named San Juan. Juan de Oñate made it his capital for a time. Runners went out daily from the new capital with orders for the pueblos. Each pueblo was to bring in corn to feed the Spanish soldiers and settlers. Already several Indians, among them women, had been whipped for refusing to give up the last of the corn they had saved. In a nearby pueblo two men were hung from trees for refusing to show the Spanish soldiers where their corn was stored.

A short time after the conquest, several soldiers came to Kishtaya to take some of the men to work at San Juan on the church the Spaniards were building. The War Chief and a few other men obeyed the order and followed the soldiers. Two soldiers remained behind to get another half-dozen men. These Kishtayans begged to be allowed to finish their work in the fields. Immediately a soldier struck one of them with his heavy leather whip. The Indian, who had never been struck before, went mad with anger. He grabbed the soldier's horse by the bridle, while the others lifted their hoes and attacked both soldiers. The Spaniards toppled off their horses, and the Indians finished them off with their stone knives. Then they pulled out the soldiers' sharp knives, cut off their scalps, and threw the bodies into the river.

Two Kishtayans mounted the horses and, with the scalps swinging on the soldiers' swords, started back to the pueblo. They were returning victorious from a battle, to be received at the pueblo with the customary honors due to victors.

One of the men ran ahead to announce the victory. With the war cry "Ai-ai," he hastened to spread the news that two Spaniards had been killed in battle. As was the custom, the women and girls rushed out to meet the war party, with songs and dances of victory. The women had put on their best *mantas*. The wives of the two men who had killed the soldiers took the scalps and went to the head of the procession.

The Kishtayans were happy to get the scalps of palefaces, since they believed that the scalps would now work their magic for the Indians and help overcome the conquerors.

The two men who had scalped the Spaniards followed behind. They did not join in the celebration, since the Indians believed that anyone who had killed an enemy must fast and cleanse himself before resuming the normal life of the pueblo.

The procession had reached the narrow path that led up the mesa when a galloping mass of Spanish soldiers caught up with them. Swooping down upon them, swinging their swords and firing into the crowd, the soldiers rode their horses

right over the people, trampling and killing.

Tied to long ropes, trailing behind the horses, were the bodies of the War Chief and the other men from Kishtaya who had gone to work at San Juan. Thick smoke rose from the river where the Spaniards had set the fields afire to burn Kishtaya's crops. A few soldiers now rushed up to the pueblo. They dragged out the old men and women and babies, too weak or too young to join in the celebration, and slashed them with their swords. In a few hours nothing living remained

of what had been the peaceful, thriving pueblo of Kishtaya.

The destruction of Kishtaya frightened the rest of the River pueblos. There was nothing left for them to do but submit peacefully to the conquerors and try to survive as best they could by learning to live with the enemy.

The Spanish settlers picked out the best lands for themselves. It was no use complaining, for any of the Indians who complained were suspected of rebellion, and the Spanish soldiers took them away to work in the mission fields. So the men stopped complaining to the conquerors. They cleared new fields and tried to raise enough food to tide them over from one harvest to the next.

Harvest followed harvest with most of it going to the conquerors. The River Indians learned to dig better irrigation ditches with the new metal tools the Spaniards brought. They plowed their fields with plows the Spaniards taught them to make. But even though their harvests were larger, the Indians had less food than ever before.

The Spaniards had brought with them several thousand sheep, cattle, and horses. Little by little the Indians got some of these animals too, but they were forbidden to own horses. The men learned to grow wheat, melons, and chili peppers. They planted peach, apricot, and apple orchards.

Spanish missionaries visited the pueblos constantly. They told the people that they must no longer worship in the ways of their fathers. They must be baptized and must worship in the church of the Spaniards. The Indians began to send their children to the mission schools and to attend church services every Sunday, but they kept up their own religion in secret.

As time went on, the Spaniards became more and more confident that the Indians had accepted their sovereignty, and they relaxed their watchfulness. More than eighty years passed peacefully, but during these four generations the hatred felt by the Indians for the Spanish conquerors grew. The people waited for the right time to rebel.

In 1680, a leader arose among the River Indians. His Spanish name was Popé. Traveling from pueblo to pueblo, Popé spoke to the chiefs and won them over to his plan. The plan called for united action on the part of all the River pueblos. They armed in secret. They were to strike together on August 13, 1680, and kill all the Spaniards—settlers, soldiers, and missionaries —and free their lands from the conquerors.

A few days before the date set for the revolt,

Popé learned that an Indian had revealed the plot to a Spanish priest during confession. "All the pueblos on the Rio Grande," the man had said, "also the Hopi to the west and the Zuni to the south, are planning a revolt. We want our lands back. We want to go back to our old ways and worship our gods as our forefathers did."

Popé sent out runners to the pueblos ordering an attack at once. The Indians struck at dawn on August 10, 1680, taking the Spaniards completely by surprise.

From Taos southward, the Indians of each pueblo shot and killed every Spaniard in their neighborhood. Then the men in their war paint rushed toward Santa Fe, which had become the capital of New Mexico in 1610. They expected to face the biggest Spanish strength there. The Indians of the pueblos to the south, west, and east, together with their Hopi, Zuni, and Apache allies, killed all the Spanish settlers near them and then dashed northward toward Santa Fe.

Santa Fe was then a town of less than a thousand Spanish inhabitants. When the news of the revolt reached them, all who could crowd into the governor's palace—men, women, and children—flocked into it. The governor's palace, which still stands today, was built like a fortress, and the Spaniards thought it would withstand Indian bows and arrows. The rest of the people barred the doors and windows of their homes, expecting the worst to happen.

Santa Fe had been caught unprepared. Firewood, food, and water were always brought into town from the outside. The Indians knew that and knew that the town could not hold out long.

By late afternoon the warriors had completely surrounded the governor's palace. Men and horses were milling around. Volley after volley of arrows was shot over the wall into the patio of the palace and into the windows and doors. Inside, lurking behind the windows and thick walls, Spanish soldiers and men were shooting into the mass of Indians. Man after man toppled over, as horses reared and fell with their riders. The sweating, tired warriors picked up the wounded and the dead, carried them off, and laid them in nearby fields. The dead were covered and left.

The medicine men tried to help the wounded with chants and to stop their bleeding with crude bandages.

The siege of Santa Fe lasted for ten days. At last, with water and food supplies exhausted, the remaining Spaniards begged to be allowed to leave the country and go south to Mexico. Led by their Spanish governor, Otermin, the Spaniards fled from New Mexico.

The Spaniards reported that four hundred colonists and twenty-one priests had been killed by the rebels. We do not know how many Indians died during this revolt. The total must have run into the hundreds. In the days following there was great mourning in many of the pueblos for fathers and sons killed at Santa Fe.

Now the Spanish conquerors were gone at last. New Mexico was Indian territory once more and the people were free to go back to their old ways of living.

But peace was short-lived. The following year Otermin marched up the Rio Grande with fire and sword, burning the pueblos along the route and destroying the cornfields. But this time the Spaniards found most of the pueblos deserted. The people had fled and were hiding in the woods and mountains to the west. The Spanish soldiers found the hidden stores of corn, beans, and dried fruit and these stores were looted and burned, but the plan of recapturing the pueblos for Spain had to be abandoned.

In 1692 another Spanish invasion of New Mexico took place. A Spaniard whose name was Diego de Vargas Zapata Juan de Leon set out from El Paso in late August with a small army of sixty soldiers and about one hundred Indian allies. So sure was he of success in reconquering the territory lost in the revolt of 1680, that he started out without the full permission of the Spanish viceroy of Mexico. He even planned to pay for the expedition out of his own pocket. Vargas knew that he would be richly rewarded by the king of Spain if he succeeded.

Vargas also knew that the Indians could not be frightened into submission and he planned his strategy carefully. He started up the Rio Grande with gentle words of forgiveness and peace— words the Pueblo Indians were anxious to hear. In the twelve years since their revolt, many pueblos had been destroyed, thousands of people had died of starvation. The roving Apache bands had given them no peace. To add to their misery, there had been a long drought that burned up the cornfields.

To a people as religious as these Pueblo Indians, this was a sign that the spirits were displeased. Had they done wrong in banishing the Spaniards and refusing to pray to the white God?

When Vargas' small army came with words of peace, promising forgiveness to all the people provided they promised to obey the king of Spain, many of the chiefs advised their people to accept Spanish sovereignty. Soon the people of other pueblos, who had fled, returned and swore allegiance to Vargas. They did not want to spend the winter in makeshift shelters, and they set to work rebuilding their ruined homes.

Building and repairing of homes spread throughout all the pueblos. The men helped with the brick making and brought in the heavy logs for the frames and roofs. The women were busy mixing clay for plastering the walls inside and out. Children went along with their mothers to bring in firewood. All knew that food would be scarce. In the late fall, women and girls went to the woods to gather edible plants and roots, berries and nuts. Perhaps with some rabbit hunting, they would manage to keep from starving till next year's crops were raised.

The victorious Vargas wrote a long report to the viceroy in Mexico. "I have conquered for God and Your Majesty," he wrote, "*all* the pueblos, without shedding a drop of blood, and I have baptized a thousand children born during the rebellion." Vargas asked for one hundred soldiers and fifty families of settlers to root the Spanish into New Mexican soil. He also recommended that the government send some miners and mechanics from the Mexican jails to teach the Pueblo Indians.

The Spanish had come to stay.

8

THE RIO GRANDE PUEBLOS TODAY

DURING the seventeenth, eighteenth, and half of the nineteenth century, the River Indians lived under Spanish rule. Always there was some fighting that kept the Spanish soldiers and settlers on the alert. The Apache and Navaho raided everywhere. The Hopi Indians were restless and, like the Apache, fought the Spaniards as well as the River pueblos. Often Hopi and Apache joined forces and together raided the Spaniards and Pueblo Indians.

In 1810, Mexico revolted against Spain. Taking advantage of the troubles Spain was having both in Latin America and in Europe, the United States government sent its explorers toward the West.

By the time Mexico won its independence from Spain, the Santa Fe Trail was operating full force and the weakened Spanish government of New Mexico could do nothing to stop it. Long caravans of dusty covered wagons toiled and rumbled across the prairies from Independence, Missouri, over the Raton Pass to Santa Fe. Homesteaders with their belongings piled high and their small children bouncing in the covered wagons, their tired cattle following behind, came year after year seeking homes.

For sixty years the Santa Fe Trail made history and legend. Then the railroad was built and gradually the trail was given up because of the greater speed and safety of railroad travel. By 1880 the Santa Fe Trail had become a memory.

Meanwhile, the United States faced war with Mexico in 1846. The quarrel came up because Mexico felt the United States was trespassing on its territory in Texas. The Mexican War came to an end in 1848, and the United States acquired for fifteen million dollars the rights to all the land north of the Rio Grande that had belonged to Spain. The river became the boundary between the United States and Mexico. So the River pueblos became the concern of the United States. At first the Indians were thought of as wards of the government, but in 1934 they were granted full citizenship like all other persons born in the United States.

In 1863 the western half of New Mexico was organized into the territory of Arizona. Homesteaders were welcomed into the new territory, and where the Indians stood in the way, Indian agents appointed by the Federal government tried to make treaties with them. The government thought it best to put all of the Indians on reservations.

Having had their experience with the Spanish conquerors, the River Indians remained wary of the new conquerors. However, they received the United States troops with ceremonies. One army officer, General Kearny, received an exciting reception at the pueblo of Santo Domingo. Some distance from the pueblo several old chiefs on horseback were lined up to greet General Kearny and his staff and they rode toward Santo Domingo together. After a while a cloud of dust appeared on the horizon. One old chief warned the visitors. "This is the way our young men like to greet important visitors," he said.

A group of Indians, their bodies glistening with grease and paint, came galloping and yelling. They wore buffalo horns and eagle feathers and carried rawhide shields and spears. They dashed by the visitors, yelling their war whoops. After they passed Kearny's men, they slowed their horses and let them rest. Then they came galloping back, firing muskets and shooting arrows into the air.

The people of Santo Domingo, dressed in their fiesta costumes, lined the plaza to greet the visitors. Kearny spoke to them, promising a new freedom for the pueblos. He told them that his government wanted to live in peace with its Indian brothers and that the United States believed in justice and freedom of worship for everyone.

The River Indian chiefs replied that they, too, wanted to live in peace. They were strong and were not afraid of the might of their white brothers. But they wanted peace and they wanted to be left alone to live in the ways of their fathers and to worship as their fathers had before them.

Unfortunately, it took a long time for the agents sent by the United States government, for the teachers and doctors, to learn that these peaceful people meant just what they said. These men and women eventually did learn that they could not force the Indians into anything they did not want to do. If an Indian trusted a white man and knew him to be a friend, he was friendly and easy to work with. If he did not trust a white man, there was nothing to be done but get the white man off the Indian lands as quickly as possible.

Much has been accomplished to help the Pueblo Indians, but only by patience, understanding, and respect for their own ways. They are still living today the way they prefer to live. They have kept their ancient ways, their religion, and their languages. Most of them are poor by our standards. Much more is still to be done toward better education, better housing, more and better medical care, and suitable work for them.

Today the younger people dress as we do—jeans and shirts for the men and boys, skirts and blouses for the young women and girls. The older women throw a blanket or shawl over their shoulders when they go out. Some men and women wear shoes; many still wear moccasins that they make themselves. Moccasins are more comfortable and cheaper. All like to wear silver and turquoise jewelry, which they either get by trading with the Navaho or make themselves. There are good silversmiths among the Pueblo Indians.

The program of ceremonial events for the Rio Grande pueblos is not as rich today as it was in

ancient times, but many ceremonies are still being observed throughout all the twelve months of the year. The ceremonies on the six dates mentioned here are typical ones that have been celebrated by the River Indians for many centuries.

White and Indian visitors are welcomed into

January 23	San Ildefonso—Annual Fiesta, Buffalo Dance
July 26	Santa Ana—Annual Fiesta, Green Corn Dance
August 4	Santo Domingo—Annual Fiesta, Green Corn Dance
September 4	Isleta—Annual Fiesta, Harvest Dance
September 19	Laguna—Annual Fiesta, Harvest Dance
December 25	Taos—Deer Dance
	Santo Domingo, Tesuque, Santa Clara, and other pueblos—Dances for three days following Christmas Eve
	San Juan—Turtle Dance

the pueblos to watch the ceremonials. The Pueblo Chief, or the governor of the pueblo, as he is now called, and his assistants keep an eye on the visitors. They see to it that all strangers remain in the plaza. Parts of each ceremony are too sacred to be seen by outsiders.

The streets of the River pueblos today are still unpaved, just as they were in the old days. There is electricity in many of the homes and most pueblos have water pumps. Children and women carry the water home in pails. Some pueblos still get their water from the river. Many women still like to carry burdens on their heads. The women often carry their babies in shawls on their backs, and they find it more convenient to carry the loaded basket or water jar on the head.

During the Green Corn Dance at Santo Domingo we were invited by an Indian friend to see his new house, which he had built himself in his free time when he was not working his land or caring for his cattle and horses. His family—

mother, wife, son, and baby girl—were home
when we stepped over the heavy threshold of the
adobe house. It was a hot August day but the
house was cool. We all breathed in the peculiar
mixture of adobe, buckskin, and juniper-smoke
smells characteristic of an Indian house. We
stepped into a room used as both kitchen and din-
ing room. Shiny linoleum covered the floor. The
room was furnished with a table, four kitchen
chairs, a high chair, and a wood stove, but there
was no icebox or sink. Three *metates* occupied the
back wall of the kitchen. These pueblo women
still prefer to grind their own corn meal. They
say it tastes better than the meal ground at a mill.

Between the kitchen and living room was a
cone-shaped fireplace. This and the stove kept the
family warm in winter. In the living room were
a chest of drawers and two beds covered with
bright patchwork quilts. On the far wall of the
room hung the rug hanger—a heavy pole filled
with fringed blankets and rugs. The rugs today
are made mostly by Navaho women, and the

River Indians trade their corn, beans, and peppers for them.

On one side of the room hung a cradle suspended from the ceiling by four heavy cords. The baby was in it and our friend's mother sat on the bed, humming a song to put the baby to sleep. The old lady was stringing a necklace of dyed corn kernels and squash seeds to be worn at the Green Corn Dance.

Beyond the kitchen was another small, dark room—the storage room, where corn was stacked against the walls. In a far corner lay a medicine bundle wrapped in a white cotton cloth. A large ceremonial drum was also carefully covered with a piece of cloth. Overhead, stuck in the small spaces between the rounded beams that supported the ceiling, were small bunches of spruce twigs and feathers used in ceremonies.

Our friend's wife asked us to sit down, and the son brought in chairs from the kitchen. The old lady said something and the younger woman jumped up. "Excuse me, I forgot my bread," she said and rushed out of the house to the cone-shaped adobe oven which she herself had made in the yard behind the house.

The night before, she had mixed wheat flour, water, salt, and yeast in a large bowl, kneading it till the mixture was smooth. She let it stand overnight and by morning the dough had risen to the brim of the bowl. Then she made a fire of dry brush in her oven and kept it burning till the oven was thoroughly heated. While the oven was heating, she kneaded the dough in the bowl once more and shaped handfuls of it into round loaves. Then she swept the oven clean with a broom made of bunch grass. Placing the loaves on a wooden paddle with a long handle, she slid them into the oven and closed the small oven door with a slab of stone, to make sure no heat would escape before the bread was baked.

Now the bread was ready. The woman slipped the paddle under the baked loaves and slid them out of the oven. She put them into a large yucca basket and carried them in. The whole house was filled with the good sweet smell of fresh bread. The old lady brought a plate from the kitchen

shelf, and our friend's wife broke a steaming loaf into chunks and put them on it. She offered the fresh bread to us. The crisp golden crust tasted better than any bread I had ever eaten.

Before our friend and his family began to eat, each of them pinched bits of crust off their bread and threw them into the fireplace. They were making a thanksgiving offering to the spirits who, they believe, are still watching over the Rio Grande Indians today, just as they did in ancient times.

Chief Pueblos of the Rio Grande

Cochiti (koh'chee-tee)

Isleta (ees-lay'tah)

Jemez (hay'mayss)

Nambe (nahm-bee')

Picuris (pick'oo-riss)

Pojoaque (poh-hwah'kih)

San Felipe (sahn feh-lee'puh)

San Ildefonso (sahn eel-duh-fohn'so)

San Juan (sahn hwahn')

Sandia (sahn-dee'uh)

Santa Ana (sahn'tah ahn'ah)

Santa Clara (sahn'tah klahr'ah)

Santo Domingo (sahn'toh doh-ming'goh)

Taos (tah'ohss)

Tesuque (teh-soo'kih)

Zia (also Sia) (see'ah)

INDEX

* Indicates illustrations.